Y0-BQU-950

Ju
296.3
K62   Kipper, Morris.
b   God's wonderful
        world.

Temple Israel Library
Minneapolis, Minn.

———

Please sign your full name on the above
card.

Return books promptly to the Library or
Temple Office.

Fines will be charged for overdue books
or for damage or loss of same.

God's Wonderful World

by MORRIS and LENORE KIPPER

Illustrated by Audrey Komrad

SHENGOLD PUBLISHERS, INC.
New York

JU
296.3
K62
b

Library of Congress Catalog Card Number: 68-56182
Published by Shengold Publishers, Inc., New York
Text: Copyright © 1968 by Morris and Lenore Kipper
Illustrations: Copyright © by Audrey Komrad
All rights reserved
Printed in the United States of America

70-66   1-26-69   REL. SCH.   350/280

To Avi

Acknowledgments

To Dr. Sylvan D. Schwartzman, Professor of Jewish Religious Education at the Hebrew Union College—Jewish Institute of Religion, who gave us the inspiration for this book;

To the students of the Religious Schools of Temple Beth Sholom, Peabody, Mass., Temple Judea, Coral Gables, Fla., and Temple Beth Sholom, Miami Beach, Fla., who used the material in this book through the seven years of experimentation that yielded the finished work;

To Judy Kreutzer and Marcia Leventhal, dedicated teachers who developed a Teacher's Guide for this book;

To the many other primary grade teachers who checked the text for concept evaluation and vocabulary level;

To Doris Feder of Coral Gables, and Reene Kreincses of New York, for patiently typing and re-typing each improved edition;

To Gertrude Hirschler, Editor, for her unfailing cooperation and invaluable counsel;

To Moshe Sheinbaum, President of Shengold Publishers, whose excellent taste will never be equalled by a committee;

Our thanks go also to the Central Conference of American Rabbis for their kind permission to quote passages from the *Union Songster*.

And *aharon aharon haviv*, to all our friends and colleagues who gave us advice and encouragement throughout.

Dear Boys and Girls,

Have you ever asked about God? Does he live in a house or on the clouds? How can God see and hear everything? Why can't *you* see God? Is God in space? If you fly to the Moon, will you find God there?

Some of the leaders and teachers of the Jewish People thought a lot about the very same things. They wrote their thoughts in Jewish books like the Torah and the Talmud. They came to know about God's ways after much looking and thinking about the world around them.

In this book, you will meet two children who also discover many things about God's ways, through looking and thinking about God's creations. Parents and teachers keep on asking questions about God. When they do this, they keep learning more about God. Now that you are older, you can discover some things about God by yourself. As you read the stories in this book, keep on looking, and thinking and asking, and each day you will find out a little bit more about God's wonderful world.

Rabbi Morris A. Kipper

THE STORY OF GENESIS

When God first made the world,
He made it full of light;
The sun to shine by day,
The moon and the stars by night.
And God saw that it was good.

He made it full of beauty;
Flowers and trees, fields and brooks.
And God saw that it was good.

He made it full of things to use;
Fruit and milk, iron and gold.
And God saw that it was good.

He made it full of living things;
Some that walk and some that fly,
Some that swim and some that creep.
And God saw that it was good.

To crown it all, the Lord made man;
With mind and heart, with hands and will,
To love and to think, to work and to play.

(Union Songster, p. 77)

And God saw everything that he had made,
And behold, it was very good.

(Genesis 1:31)

JOEY MEETS OSSIE

"God made mountains and hills and covered them with grass. God makes the rains and dew to fall and causes the seeds to sprout to plants."

From the Midrash (Exod. Rabbah)

The Rabbis who lived many years ago wrote a story about a visit Moses and Aaron paid to Pharaoh, the King of Egypt. "Who is your God that I should listen to him?" the King asked them. "The Universe is filled with the might and power of our God," they replied. Then Moses and Aaron explained to the King that all the wonders of nature—the mountains, the grass, the rains, the planets and much more—show us the works of God.

Have you ever had a strange dream? Can you sometimes do things in dreams that you cannot do when you are awake? When you wake up, can you always remember what happened in your dream? Joey is a boy who likes to experiment, explore and discover. In this story Joey has a strange adventure and he finds out how he can watch God's power at work.

JOEY MEETS OSSIE

"It's time to go to bed," Mrs. Gordon said.

"Aw Mom, why can't I see another TV program? I never get a chance to see this next one," complained Joey.

"Not tonight, but after you brush your teeth you can read a while. I'll be up to turn off the light in a while. Now run along," answered his mother.

Joey turned off the TV set and went to his bedroom. After a while, Mother came in to say goodnight. Joey had fallen asleep, with the book still in his hand. She covered him with the blanket, turned off the light, and kissed him softly on the forehead.

Suddenly Joey heard a strange voice. "Ouch," said the voice. Joey looked around. He wondered where the voice came from. Something else was puzzling him. Here he was sitting up in bed eating an orange, in the middle of the night.

"Stop squeezing me, you bully!" Again that same strange voice.

"Who said that?" Joey whispered, "Where are you?"

"Right in your hand," the voice replied. "Now put me down, please!"

Joey looked at the orange in his hand. A talking orange? No, it couldn't be! He must be dreaming.

"Help! Now see what you've done. Pick me up!" the strange voice insisted.

Joey was really puzzled now. The orange was still in his hand, but that's not where the voice came from.

"Down here, Joey! Down here!"

He got on his knees and started looking for the voice. All he could see was an orange seed that had fallen on the floor. He picked it up and was about to throw it into the trash can.

"Hey, don't do that!"

Joey was surprised. This little seed was the strange voice he had been looking for.

"Let's be friends," said the little seed. "My name is Orange Seed, but my friends call me Ossie. Get it? O.S. for orange seed."

Joey laughed and forgot that he had been a little frightened at hearing the strange voice in the middle of the night. "And my name's Joey."

"Hi, Joey! Whew, that was a close call. You almost threw me into the garbage!"

"Well isn't that where you belong?" Joey asked.

"I beg your pardon, sir. I do *not* belong in any trash can. How would you like it if I threw you into the trash?" Ossie asked angrily.

Joey laughed. "I really don't think you could, but I'm sorry if I hurt your feelings, Ossie. It's just that we like to keep our house clean of trash."

"*Trash!* he calls me. Look here, Mr. Joey, I happen to be a miracle, made by God Himself. God created me *not* to be trash, but to grow into a big tree. Trash he calls me!" Ossie turned his back on Joey.

"I . . . I'm really sorry," Joey apologized.

At first, Ossie didn't answer. Then he said slowly, "Well, I guess I should forgive you. After all, I can't expect you humans to understand that a seed is a miracle of God. But where do you think you came from, Joey?"

Joey thought awhile and tried to remember what his father had told him. "I guess I came from a seed, too. Dad said I grew in a special place inside my mother until I got big enough to be a baby."

"Yes, you did grow from a little cell inside your mother and God made that cell grow into you," explained Ossie. "Now where do you think that orange came from?"

Joey laughed. "Don't tell me from someone's tummy!"

"Ha! Ha! Very funny," answered Ossie. "That orange came from a tree, and the tree came from a wonderful seed like me. The tree, and you too, were both planted from seeds. You grew inside your mother, and the tree was planted inside the earth."

"Well, what do you know!" laughed Joey, "Mother Earth."

"Again with the jokes," said Ossie. "But this time you strike out. Mother Earth *is* the name that many people call the good dirt plants grow in."

"Really?" asked Joey.

"Everything living has to have a mother," answered Ossie. "Plants, animals, and people grow from seeds or cells that are from plants, animals or people of the same kind. But look, kid, I'm not your teacher. All I want to do is get into some dirt so God can help me grow into an orange tree."

Joey couldn't help laughing. "Did you ever see an orange tree, Ossie? Why, it's bigger than Dad and I put together! Just how do you expect to grow into such a big thing, when you are so tiny?"

"O. K. wise guy," said Ossie. "Just plant me and you'll see. Just put me into Mother Earth. God will help me grow into a tree bigger than you or your father. Then I will grow oranges with little seeds that will grow into big trees, too."

Suddenly Joey heard another voice. He didn't have to guess about this one. It was his mother calling. "Are you ready for breakfast, Joey? Your orange juice is waiting. Better hurry, or you'll be late for school."

Joey rushed downstairs and looked through the trash can. "Mom, where did you put the seeds, the orange seeds! I need them. I have to plant them in Mother Earth!"

Joey's father put down the morning paper. "Hold on, now. First, go get washed and dressed. Then we'll talk about this seed business."

"But, Dad—

"No buts, young man. Get dressed first." Quickly Joey ran upstairs and was back down in no time at all.

"Well," his father exclaimed, "what a nice surprise!" Joey told his dream to his father. "Joey, you've planted seeds before, haven't you?"

"Sure," Joey answered, "and some of them grew and some didn't. But this time I want to be sure to watch God's power at work. When you watch a seed grow into a real plant, it's like watching God's power at work."

Joey picked up his glass of orange juice. It tasted very, very good this morning. He thought about Ossie the Seed in his dream. Ossie wanted to grow into a beautiful orange tree and grow oranges. Then the seeds in the orange would grow into more orange trees. He remembered what Ossie told him, that all of this is a miracle of God.

Joey's mother and father heard him say: "Be praised, O Lord, our God, King of the Universe, Who creates the fruit of the tree."

THE CLIMBING TREE

*"As the days of a tree are the days of my
people."*   *(Isaiah 65:22)*

The man who wrote this was a very wise man who
lived many years ago. The things he taught are part
of the Bible. After you read this story you will find
out what Isaiah meant.

Do you have a special place you like to go where
you can play your favorite make-believe games? Is it
a club house, a special corner in your house, or maybe
a special tree? One morning Debbie Berman and Joey
Gordon find out that something terrible is happening
to their "special place."

THE CLIMBING TREE

Bzzz——— Bzzz——— Bzzz——— Bzzz———

Debbie rubbed her eyes. "What a loud noise to wake me up," she thought, "and it isn't even time to get up for school! Mom," she called sleepily, but no one answered. "Mom!" She raised her voice. Still no answer. Finally she shouted, "Mom, what's going on?"

But Mrs. Berman couldn't hear Debbie because the noise outside was too loud. So Debbie went downstairs and looked out through the living room window.

"Oh no," she cried. Quickly she ran to find her mother in the kitchen. Before Mrs. Berman could say

"Good morning" Debbie was asking questions. "Why is that man on top of the tree? Why is he cutting off the branches? Where will Joey and I climb now? It's not fair!"

When Debbie quieted down, and her mother had finished stirring the cereal, Mrs. Berman explained that the tree had to be cut. A disease of some kind had made the trunk rot. It no longer would be safe to climb the tree. Debbie was angry at first, then sad at the thought of losing her favorite tree. She understood why it had to be taken down, but she and Joey, who lived next door, would miss it very much. Debbie and Joey Gordon had been friends for two years. One of the things they liked best to do was climb that tree. Sometimes it was their airplane, sometimes it was their ranger station, sometimes their fort. Sometimes it was just a private quiet place to talk about a lot of things.

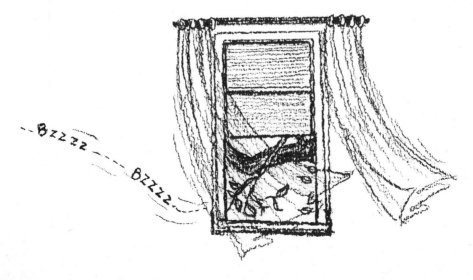

After Debbie had dressed she went to call for Joey. He was already watching the men with the saw cutting down the tree, piece by piece.

"Hi, Debbie, look at that saw go," he exclaimed.

"How can you care about that saw!" she shouted angrily, raising her voice above the noise. "Now all our fun is spoiled. We'll never find another tree like this one."

"Gee, I didn't think of that," answered Joey. "Yeah, it's not fair. Why does it have to be our tree?"

Soon all that was left of their beautiful tree was a little short stump. Debbie went to look at the stump.

"Come here, Joey, look at these rings. Some are big and some are small. I wonder how they got there." While they were busy looking at the tree stump, one of the workmen came over.

"Sorry kids. You'll have to find another favorite tree." Then he looked more closely at the tree stump. "Say, this was a pretty old tree."

"How do you know?" the children asked.

"Why, those rings tell how long this tree was alive."

"Alive?" questioned Joey. "You mean like Debbie and me?"

"Of course." The workman told them how the rings are made each year the tree grows. The wide rings tell us that the tree's growth that year was good. The narrow rings show that the tree's growth that year was not so good.

"Then how old is *this* tree?" asked Joey.

All three of them began to count the rings. But the workman had to leave with his truck, so Debbie and Joey counted and counted and counted.

"Wow," Debbie said. "One hundred fifty years old!" She tried to think of someone who was that old, but she couldn't.

Joey was still counting, then looked up and said, "You're wrong, it's one hundred forty-two years old."

"No, it's not," argued Debbie.

"Yes, it is," answered Joey.

"I say one hundred fifty years!"

"Oh yeah? Well, you're wrong. Go buy some glasses!" Joey shouted.

"Is that so? Well, Smarty, who got an A in arithmetic?"

"Hey, what's this shouting about?" asked Dr. Berman. He was on his way to his office. Both children rushed to tell him. "Hold on," Dr. Berman said. "Wait a minute. Let's count again. This time together."

This time they both counted one hundred forty-seven rings. They smiled at each other sheepishly, knowing that they both were wrong.

"That's older than Grandma Berman," said Debbie.

Joey added, "Why, that tree was here before this city was built."

Debbie's father smiled. "Yes, Joey. There are trees around here that were alive when Columbus came to America and they are still living and growing today. One hundred forty-seven years is older than people usually get to live, but for a tree it's not so old at all. Did you know that there are some trees in California that are two and three thousand years old?"

"Then how old is the oldest living tree?" asked Debbie.

Dr. Berman told them about the Sequoia trees in California. Scientists think they are about three to four thousand years old. The children had trouble figuring out how long ago that might have been. Joey remembered having learned that the story of the Jewish people was very old too. He asked if the Sequoias had already been living in the days of Abraham, the first Jew.

"Good for you, Joey!" Debbie's father replied. "The oldest living tree is about four thousand years old and the Rabbis taught us that the story of the Jewish people began about that time, too."

"Gosh, do you think Abraham might have planted that tree?" asked Debbie.

"That's great!" said Joey. "Abraham, the first Jew, planted the oldest living tree."

Dr. Berman laughed as he got into his car. "Not exactly, Joey. Abraham and all the other leaders of the Jewish people we learn about lived in another part of the world than the place where that tree still lives and grows. But they did live at the same time when that tree was just a sapling. Oh my, look at the time! I'll be late for work if I don't hurry. See you later kids."

On the way to school Debbie and Joey talked some more about those very old trees.

"I can't imagine four thousand years ago, can you, Joey?"

"I can't either, but it must have been a long, long, long time ago." For a while they walked without saying anything. Joey was puzzled that a tree could live so long. It was living when Abraham, the first Jew, was alive and it was still alive, right now, as he walked to school. Debbie thought it was wonderful that God made the Sequoia trees and the story of the Jewish people live all those years, right up to this very day. It reminded her of a prayer she heard often; *Praised be His Name Whose glorious Kingdom is forever and ever.*

As the children turned the corner Joey ran ahead and shouted, "Look, I'll bet this tree is one hundred years old." He started to climb up.

"Joey, come down! We'll be late for school," Debbie scolded. As they passed each tree along the way they saw how each one was so different from the other. Some had thick trunks, some narrow, some stood straight and some were bent over. They played a guessing game about how old each tree might be.

"You know what, Joey? I guess if we look hard enough we'll find another favorite tree." They both laughed and got to the school entrance just as the first bell rang.

Debbie and Joey had lost their favorite climbing tree but they were thankful that God made so many different kinds of beautiful trees that they could sometimes climb, sometimes look at and sometimes just sit under to cool off on a hot day.

JOEY'S COOKOUT

*"God's Kingdom is an everlasting kingdom
and it continues throughout all generations."
(Psalms 145:13)*

This was written a long time ago and became part of our Bible. What do you think the psalmist* was thinking of when he spoke of God's Kingdom? A king is the ruler over a certain country, a certain place we can find on this earth. Where is the Kingdom of God? It is also written in the Bible that the universe "belongs to the Lord your God...the earth and all there is on it." (Deut. 10:14) When we look up into the skies we can see many things. But there is even more that we cannot see.

Debbie and Joey have already discovered some of the ways God's power works in making things grow. Now they find out some of the ways in which God's power works in the heavens. They discover how one of God's creations helped make a new invention.

* A psalmist is like a poet who can say his thoughts about God in a beautiful way.

JOEY'S COOKOUT

Debbie was sitting on her porch reading a book when she smelled hamburgers cooking. What a good smell!

Then she heard Joey, from next door, call, "Debbie, come and see something great!"

She ran to his yard and saw a strange-looking thing with hamburgers on it. She walked around it, saw the hamburgers cooking, but couldn't see any fire or charcoal.

"What is this? Where's the fire?" she asked.

"Isn't it great? It's a new kind of cooker," Joey said excitedly. "It's a Solar stove."

"A what?" asked Debbie.

"A Solar stove. The sun is cooking our hamburgers."

Joey's mother had just come outdoors with another tray of hamburgers. "Hello, Debbie. How do you like our new cooker?"

"It's great. But how does it work?"

"We're not really sure we understand, but we know that this stove *catches* the heat of the sun and cooks our hamburgers," Mrs. Gordon replied.

Debbie didn't understand at all. "But the sun is so far away. How can it cook hamburgers?"

Joey knew a lot about the stars and planets and things in the sky. It was something he had read about often. "The sun isn't so far away. It's only ninety-three million miles away from Earth."

"Only ninety-three million miles. Who says that's not far!" answer **said** Debbie.

"Well, it's farther than the moon, but any other sun is much farther from us than our sun," explained Joey.

"What other sun?" Debbie was puzzled. She had never heard that before.

"All the stars are suns, too, and they are not as close to us as our sun," Joey proudly explained.

"That's right, Debbie; all the stars are burning balls of fire just like our sun," Mrs. Gordon added.

"Then why don't those other stars cook our hamburgers?" asked Debbie.

Boy, girls don't know anything, Joey thought. "Because they aren't close enough, silly!" he said aloud.

Debbie looked at the hamburgers and began to laugh. "I think our sun *is too close* to the Earth."

"Girls! What do they know about the sun and stars? Who told you that the sun is too close to the Earth?"

"No one told me," she giggled. "I just *know* that the sun is too close and *too hot.*"

"How do you know that? Venus is too close to the sun and Mars may be too far, but the *Earth* is *just right.*"

Debbie giggled again and argued. "No, the sun is *too hot.*"

Joey was really angry with her now. "Okay, Smarty, tell me how *you know* that!"

Because right now the sun is burning your hamburgers," she laughed and laughed.

"Oh, no!" shouted Joey, as he tried to save his burned hamburgers.

After they cleaned up the mess of burned hamburgers, they tried again. Joey put some more hamburgers on the cooker.

"Well," Joey said, "Too bad our hamburgers burned, but the sun is still just far enough away so that the Earth won't burn, or freeze either. Luckily for us, God put the planet Earth in just the right place."

They watched the hamburgers, very carefully this time. They talked some more about the sun and stars. "Can you guess how many stars like our sun there are?" Mother asked.

"A hundred?" Debbie guessed.

"No!" said Joey, "A thousand?"

After a few more guesses, Debbie suddenly got very excited. She thought she knew the right answer. "I know! There are as many stars in the sky as there are people in the whole world!"

"You're on the right track, now," smiled Mrs. Gordon. "Try to think how many grains of sand there are on all the beaches of the Earth. One scientist thinks there are as many stars in the sky as there are grains of sand on all the beaches on the Earth."

"That would be *zillions* and *zillions!*" Joey said.

"More than we can know," said Debbie.

"And did God make all those stars, too? And all those grains of sand?"

"Boy!" exclaimed Joey, "We're pretty lucky to be in such a special place in God's Universe. God is really good to us."

Just then, Joey looked at the Solar stove. "Hurry up, go get the buns, the ketchup and the mustard. The hamburgers are done. Just right, this time." They all laughed.

Joey gave one to Debbie. "MMM—very, very good, thanks, Joey."

"Don't forget to thank God, who gave us the sun and who teaches us to use the things He created."

They both said. "Thank you God, King of the Universe, Who creates our food from the earth."

THE DETECTIVES

"They shall speak of the glory of Your Kingdom and talk of Your Power."

(Psalms 145:11)

This psalm tells us that if we look at God's creations we will discover some of God's great power.

Debbie and Joey have already come to know a little about God's great power. They know about the special unseen power inside a seed that makes it possible for the seed to grow into a plant. They know about the unseen power we call gravity that keeps the sun in the sky and the earth in its place in space. Have you ever tried to look for something you can't see? In this story Debbie and Joey are about to discover another unseen power in God's Kingdom.

THE DETECTIVES

One weekend Debbie's little cousin Judy came to spend the night at Debbie's house. The two girls woke up very early. They enjoyed sitting around in their pajamas, playing with their games and fixing their own breakfast. After breakfast, they enjoyed watching their favorite television shows until Mr. and Mrs. Berman were up.

This morning, as they were watching television, they heard the weatherman say, "Well, folks, the wind will really be around today. You can look for a *strong wind* due to reach our city around noon. Skies will be cloudy, and we may have some rain."

That afternoon, after lunch, little Judy was outdoors.

"Hi, Judy! Is Debbie home?" It was Joey.

Judy didn't answer. Instead, she kept looking and
searching for something.

"Hey, Judy, what are you doing?"

"I'm looking for something, Joey," Judy said.

"Wait, I'll help you. Did you lose something?"
asked Joey.

"No, I didn't lose anything," Judy answered,
"I'm looking for a strong wind. The weatherman said
it was coming this afternoon, but I can't find it."

Joey laughed to himself. Just then Debbie came out. "Hi, Joey! What's so funny?"

"Your cousin's looking for a strong wind," Joey whispered, with a knowing smile. The two of them thought that was very funny, because they knew better; but Judy, who was only three, asked, "Will you help me, Joey and Debbie? Will you help me find the strong wind?"

They played along with little Judy in a make-believe game.

"Okay," Joey said, sounding like a policeman. "Now, you look in the back yard, Debbie. You look in the front yard, Judy, and I'll go look in my yard."

"Did you find the strong wind, Debbie?" Joey asked when they returned.

"Not I," she answered.

"Did you find the strong wind, Judy?"

Not I," she answered.

"Well, we'd better search some more," Joey ordered.

But little Judy seemed puzzled. Finally, she asked, "What does a strong wind look like?"

"You mean you don't know what it looks like?" Debbie giggled. "Then how can we find it?"

"I know," little Judy said, "let's call the weatherman and ask him!"

Debbie and Joey couldn't help laughing. Mrs. Berman came out. "Well, what's the big joke?"

Judy ran to her and said, "Can we call the weatherman, please? Can we?"

When Debbie and Joey told her the story, Mrs. Berman smiled. She put her arm around Judy. "It's windy today, just as the weatherman said. We won't be able to find the wind. If we look carefully, we can *search* for what the wind can do. Look up at the sky. See the clouds? Are they moving? Look here on the lawn. See the leaves moving? Look at the trees. See them swaying? What else can you think of?"

"The wind keeps my kite in the sky," said Joey.

"And the wind makes a sailboat move," said Debbie.

"You mean I can't ever *see* the strong wind?" Judy finally said.

"That's right!" Mrs. Berman replied. "You can't see the wind, but you know it's there because *you can see and feel what it does.*"

Joey remembered something he had learned in school. "Yeah, that's just like the air around us. We need it. We use it. We feel it. But we can't see it."

He wondered about the wind and the air you can't see. He wondered if that was the way it was with God. "Can we see what God does?"

Well, Joey, that's quite a question," said Mrs. Berman. "Now, let's begin with you and Judy. God makes little boys and girls for mothers and fathers to love and care for. God gives us the birds that sing, the bread we eat. God set out the stars at night and the sun every day. That is why we call God the Creator of the Universe. And most important of all, God helps us to love other people, and to know right from wrong, because there's a little bit of God's goodness in each one of us."

"That's wonderful," sighed Debbie. "I can't see God, but I know God is here, there and everywhere, because I can see what God does, and sometimes I think I can feel God, when I've done something very good."

Just then Joey shouted, "Hey, Debbie, Judy, look at the sky! Wow, look at those dark clouds! They sure are moving fast."

Suddenly, his hat blew off.

"Oops! Catch my hat!"

Then Judy's scarf blew off and she began to chase it. The rain began to come down very fast, now.

"Hurry, children," Debbie's mother called, "that *strong wind has* come and it brought the rain clouds, too!"

When they were inside and dried off, little Judy said, *"We* didn't find the strong wind, but *it* sure found us!"

THE GREAT SEARCH

*"Stand still and consider the wondrous works
of God."*   *(Job 37:14)*

There is a story the Rabbis tell about Abraham, the first Jew. When he was a baby, he was hidden in a cave for three years to keep him safe from King Nimrod. When he left the cave he thought about all the things he saw around him. He saw the moon whose brightness lit up the darkness of night. "This must be God," he said, and he worshipped the moon all night long. But in the morning the moon went away, and the sun rose in its place. "This must be God, then," he said, and he worshipped the sun all day long. But in the evening the sun went away and the moon came back. And now Abraham saw all the stars and planets in the sky. Then he exclaimed, "Surely, God is none of these. They must all have one Master and God to guide them!"

In this story, Joey, like Abraham, is thinking about the wonderful works of God. By watching and thinking about the things around him, Joey discovers he can come to know a little about the way the power of God is at work in the world around us.

THE GREAT SEARCH

The night of the big rainstorm Joey had a strange dream. He and Debbie and Judy were sitting under a big tree on a hill in the countryside. They were searching for something. They bent down close to the ground. Joey asked, "Earth, are you the Giver of Life, the mother of all living things?"

"Do not call me God," the earth replied. "By myself, I am nothing. Alone, I am dry and hard as rock. It is only when the rain falls and trickles down between the grains of soil that the roots of a tree can get at my riches."

Rain had begun to fall. The children stood up, and Debbie stretched out her arms to feel the cool drops of rain. "Life-giving water," she asked, "Are you my God?"

"Do not call me God," the rain replied. "Alone, I am nothing. It is only when I am kept moving that I can bring life. First, I am a cloud. Then, I fall as rain and sink down into the earth. The tree roots pull me up to the trunk and out into the leaves. Then the winds lift me off the leaves and I rise as mist into the sky, where I become a cloud again."

The children stood up straight, letting the wind blow through their hair. "Winds, winds, are you my God?" little Judy asked.

"Do not praise us," the winds replied. "Alone, we are nothing. Look up into the sky. It is the sun that really brings life. Without its warmth, there wouldn't be a single living thing upon earth."

The children looked up to the sun. It felt warm on their faces. "Sun, O Sun," Joey asked, "Is your face the face of God?"

Then down from the sun, the sunbeams replied: "Do not call the sun God. Alone, it is nothing. It withers and burns living things. The winds and the rains and the earth must always be helping each other.

But even all of us together, the earth, the rain, the winds and the sun, we would be powerless if there were not something else, even greater than all of us together, that gives the power of life."

Now the children turned to the big tree beneath which they were standing under. "O Tree of Life," they said, "Surely you are our God."

But the tree replied, "Do not call me God. Once I was a seed so small you could have held me in your hand. Within that seed was the power and life that is in me now."

Then the earth, the rain, the wind, the sun and the tree all said together: "God is the power that is greater than all of us together. Let us adore the ever-living God, and give thanks to His name, Who spread out the heavens and made the earth, Whose glory is found in the heavens above, and Whose greatness is seen throughout the world. He is our God. There is none beside Him."

The next morning Joey woke with a strange feeling. He thought about his dream that day and many other days. Now whenever he heard the prayer, "Hear, O Israel, the Lord, our God, the Lord is One," it meant something very special to him. He thought of how God's creations came together to help one another. He remembered his dream and his search for God. He knew a little more about the greatness of God, and what he knew made him feel good.

"How Great Are Your Works, O God,
In Wisdom You have made them all.
Psalms 104:24

"TEMPLE ISRAEL"